An Educated Slice

Charles M. Schulz

Starring Snoopy as the World Famous Golfer

TOPPER BOOKS
AN IMPRINT OF PHAROS BOOKS • A SCRIPPS HOWARD COMPANY
NEW YORK

First published in 1990.

PEANUTS color panels: copyright © 1952, 1958, 1965 United
Feature Syndicate, Inc.

PEANUTS comic strips: copyright © 1970, 1972, 1974, 1976,
1977, 1980, 1981, 1982, 1983, 1984, 1985, 1986, 1987,
1988, 1989, 1990 United Feature Syndicate, Inc.

Library of Congress Catalog Card Number: 89-043716
Pharos ISBN: 0-88687-486-6

Printed in the United States of America

TOPPER BOOKS
An Imprint of Pharos Books
A Scripps Howard Company
200 Park Avenue
New York, New York 10166

10 9 8 7 6 5 4 3 2 1

Today we worked on the short irons.

HE DOESN'T SAY ANYTHING ABOUT EATING OR SLEEPING..

10-18

I WONDER WHERE YOU SLEEP WHEN YOU'RE AT GOLF CAMP..

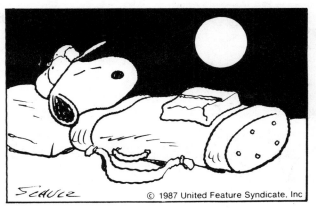

© 1987 United Feature Syndicate. Inc

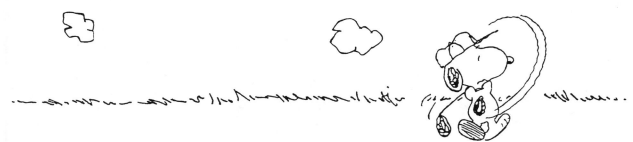

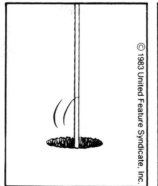

© 1986 United Feature Syndicate, Inc.

8-17

REMEMBER WHERE THE PRO SHOP IS? OKAY, RUN BACK THERE...

HERE'S WHAT I WANT YOU TO TELL THEM..

SCHULZ

© 1983 United Feature Syndicate, Inc.   7-9

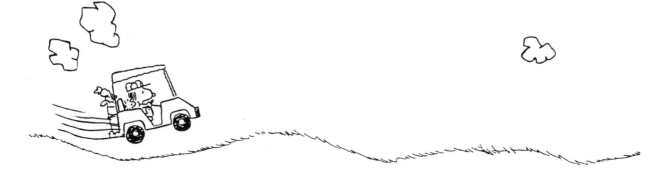

TELL CHUCK WHAT HAPPENED, MARCIE... WAIT 'TIL YOU HEAR THIS, CHUCK!

WELL, WE WERE CADDYING FOR MRS. BARTLEY AND MRS. NELSON, SEE...ALL OF A SUDDEN, ANOTHER LADY COMES BY WITH A REAL TINY LITTLE FUZZY DOG...THAT'S WHEN IT ALL HAPPENED..THAT'S WHEN SHE GOT SO UPSET...

"WHAT ARE YOU DOING WITH MY DOG?!" THE LADY SCREAMED

"I'M SORRY, MA'AM," I SAID.. "I THOUGHT IT WAS A DIVOT SO I REPLACED IT!"

HEE HEE HEE HEE

EVERY PLACE I TAKE HER, SHE EMBARRASSES ME!

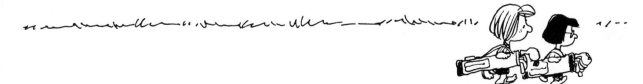

PEANUTS featuring "Good ol' Charlie Brown"

by SCHULZ

?

MY FOOT'S CAUGHT IN THE SHOE WASHER, SIR

THIS ISN'T A SHOE WASHER, MARCIE, IT'S A BALL WASHER! HERE, SLIP YOUR FOOT OUT OF YOUR SHOE...

IF YOU'RE GONNA BE A CADDY, MARCIE, YOU HAVE A LOT TO LEARN!

4-13

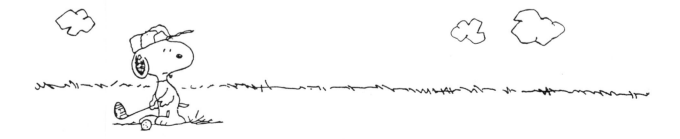

HE'S THE CRABBIEST GUY IN THE CLUB! HE THINKS MRS. BARTLEY AND MRS. NELSON PLAY TOO SLOW...

I THINK HE HATES WOMEN GOLFERS...

IS HE REALLY THE CRABBIEST PLAYER IN THE CLUB?

4-20

STAND BACK, MARCIE..THE LADIES ARE GONNA LET HIM PLAY THROUGH

I JUST WANT TO SEE WHO HE IS...

© 1980 United Feature Syndicate, Inc.

SCHULZ

HI! I'M PEPPERMINT PATTY.. I GUESS WE'RE PLAYING IN THE SAME THREESOME...

DON'T GET TOO CLOSE! YOU MIGHT STEP ON MY GOLF SHOES OR SMUDGE MY WHITE TURTLENECK...

6-22 © 1981 United Feature Syndicate, Inc.

NEVER STRIKE ANOTHER PLAYER ON THE FIRST TEE, SIR...

PEANUTS

Immediately after he won the golf tournament, he was interviewed on TV.

"This is the most exciting moment of my life!" he said.

"I saw you on TV," said his wife. "I thought the day we got married was the most exciting moment of your life."

In his next tournament, he failed to make the cut.

4 – 4

SCHULZ

THE SERGEANT HURLS HIMSELF UPON THE GRENADE TO SAVE HIS TROOPS!!

5-21

BUT A MIRACLE OCCURS..THE GRENADE FAILS TO EXPLODE...

© 1989 United Feature Syndicate, Inc.

JUST THEN, A TREMENDOUS ARTILLERY BARRAGE BEGINS, AND THE TROOPS RETREAT TO AN OASIS!

EXHAUSTED, THEY REST BENEATH A PALM TREE...

NOW, HE'S WHERE? YES, SIR.. I UNDERSTAND...

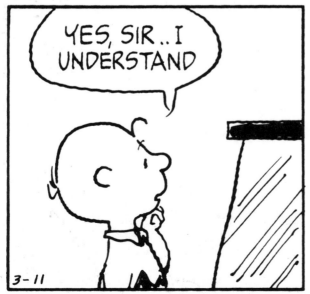

HI, MRS. NELSON.. HI, MRS. BARTLEY... ARE YOU HAVING A NICE GOLF GAME?

3-19

YES, MA'AM, I'M RAKING ALL THE SAND TRAPS...

© 1987 United Feature Syndicate, Inc.

WHY? WELL, MY DOG IS IN THE FOREIGN LEGION, SEE, AND HE WAS LEADING HIS TROOPS ACROSS THE DESERT TO FORT ZINDERNEUF, SEE, AND...

YES, YOU GO AHEAD WITH YOUR GAME..I UNDERSTAND..

START YOUR OWN
PEANUTS. GALLERY

My check for $_____ is enclosed.
Ship to:

_____
NAME

_____
ADDRESS

_____
CITY STATE ZIP

Return to: Sales Dept., Topper Books, 200 Park Avenue, New York, NY 10166.

PEANUTS COLLECTORS SERIES

☐ (#1) DOGS DON'T EAT DESSERT $5.95
☐ (#2) YOU'RE ON THE WRONG FOOT AGAIN, CHARLIE BROWN $5.95
☐ (#3) BY SUPPER POSSESSED $5.95
☐ (#4) TALK IS CHEEP, CHARLIE BROWN $5.95
☐ (#5) IT DOESN'T TAKE MUCH TO ATTRACT A CROWD $6.95
☐ (#6) IF BEAGLES COULD FLY $6.95
☐ BROTHERS & SISTERS: It's All Relative $5.95
☐ HAPPINESS IS A WARM PUPPY $5.95
☐ LOVE IS WALKING HAND IN HAND $5.95

PEANUTS JUVENILE BOOKS (Full Color Oversized Hardcovers)

☐ CHARLIE BROWN This is Your Life $7.95
☐ SALLY School is My World $7.95
☐ SCHROEDER Music is My Life $7.95
☐ SNOOPY My Greatest Adventures $7.95

__ **TOTAL BOOKS** (Please add .50 per book for postage and handling.)